Apus

Songs for children
chosen by Beatrice Harrop
Peggy Blakeley and David Gadsby

with PIANO accompaniments,
chords for GUITAR, parts for descant recorders,
glockenspiel, chime bars and percussion
and DRAWINGS by Bernard Cheese

A & C Black Ltd · London

First published 1975 by A. & C. Black Ltd 35 Bedford Row London WC1R 4JH © 1975 A. & C. Black Ltd
Reprinted 1976 (twice), 1978, 1979
ISBN 0 7136 1553 2 (spiral bound) 0 7136 1846 9 (net edition: spiral bound with covered spine)
A WORDS ONLY edition is also available ISBN 0 7136 1552 4
Printed in Great Britain by Hollen Street Press Limited, Slough, Berkshire

Contents

1 If you're happy

1   If you're happy and you know it,
    clap your hands.
    If you're happy and you know it,
    clap your hands.
    If you're happy and you know it,
    Then you'll surely want to show it,
    If you're happy and you know it,
    clap your hands.

2   If you're happy and you know it,
    nod your head . . .

3   If you're happy and you know it,
    stamp your feet . . .

4   If you're happy and you know it,
    say "Ha! Ha!" . . .

5   If you're happy and you know it,
    do all four! . . .

Children might be divided into four groups, singing the following
alternative words:
   If you're happy and you know it, play a drum
                     blow a horn
                     tap two sticks
                     hit a gong
                     do all four.

Words and music: Traditional American

2 I'd like to teach the world to sing

I'd like to build the world a home
and furnish it with love,
Grow apple trees and honey bees
and snow-white turtle doves.
I'd like to teach the world to sing
in perfect harmony,
I'd like to hold it in my arms
and keep it company.
I'd like to see the world for once
all standing hand in hand,
And hear them echo through the hills
for peace throughout the land.

CHIME BARS (OR CHIME BARS AND RECORDER)

I'd like to build_ the world_ a home_ and fur-nish it with love,_

Grow ap-ple trees and honey bees and snow-white tur-tle doves._

I'd like to teach the world_ to sing_ in perfect har-mo-ny,_

Words and music: B. Backer, B. Davis, R. Cook and R. Greenaway

The part for percussion is a build-up of

(a) note concentration per bar
(b) accent

In the first eight bars, only the first beat is played, then the first and third, and finally each note.

The part as written tends to encourage accent on the first beat of the bar and teachers may wish to adapt either this or the off-beat accent of the melody so that the two coincide.

3 I whistle a happy tune

Whenever I feel afraid,
I hold my head erect,
And whistle a happy tune
So no-one will suspect I'm afraid.

While shivering in my shoes,
I strike a careless pose
And whistle a happy tune
And no-one ever knows I'm afraid.

The result of this deception
Is very strange to tell,
For when I fool the people I fear,
I fool myself as well.

I whistle a happy tune
And every single time,
The happiness in the tune
Convinces me that I'm not afraid.

Words: Oscar Hammerstein
Music: Richard Rodgers

This tune offers a good opportunity to explain the musical form of A A B A tunes:

A You hear a tune
A To make sure you'll remember it, you hear it again
B Then, as a change, you hear a new bit of tune
A Finally, to round things off, you hear the first tune again

Teachers can give other examples of this, e.g. Old Macdonald had a farm, All through the night, Au clair de la lune and many pop songs.

To help to make it clearer for the children, they might use triangles to play the first beat of each bar in the A tunes and four beats to each bar in the B tune.

Alternatively the following idea might be tried:

Boys whistle first A tune
Girls whistle second A tune
Everyone *sings* the B tune
Everyone whistles the third A tune.

For older children the key changes in the B tune might be pointed out.

4 Yellow submarine

1 In the town where I was born
Lived a man who sailed to sea,
And he told us of his life
In the land of submarines.
So we sailed on to the sun,
Till we found the sea of green,
And we lived beneath the waves
In our yellow submarine.

    We all live in a yellow submarine,
    Yellow submarine, yellow submarine,
    We all live in a yellow submarine,
    Yellow submarine, yellow submarine.

2 And our friends are all aboard,
Many more of them live next door,
And the band begins to play
. . .

3 As we live a life of ease,
Every one of us has all we need,
Sky of blue and sea of green,
In our yellow submarine.

Words and music: John Lennon and Paul McCartney

5 Sing a rainbow

Red and yellow and pink and green,
Purple and orange and blue,
I can sing a rainbow,
Sing a rainbow,
Sing a rainbow, too.
Listen with your eyes,
Listen with your eyes
And sing everything you see.
You can sing a rainbow,
Sing a rainbow,
Sing along with me.
Red and yellow and pink and green,
Purple and orange and blue.
Now we can sing a rainbow,
Sing a rainbow,
Sing a rainbow, too.

Words and music: Arthur Hamilton

6 The super-supper march

1. Hungry, hungry, I am hungry.
   Table, table, here I come.
   I could eat a goose-moose burger,
   Fifteen pickles and a purple plum!

2. I could eat three bowls of goulash,
   Half a pound of wuzzled wheat.
   I could eat a peck of poobers,
   Then I'd really get to work and eat!

3. Oysters, noodles, strawberry stroodles,
   French fries, fish hash, one red beet.
   Lamb chops, wham chops, huckleberry mish mash,
   Oh, the things that I could eat!

4. Doughnuts, dumplings, blueberry bumplings,
   Chocolate mush-mush, super sweet.
   Clam stew, ham stew, water melon wush wush,
   Oh, the stuff that I could eat!

5. Deep dish rhubarb, upside-down cake,
   I could eat a frittered flum.
   Hungry, hungry, I am starving!
   Table, table, table, HERE I COME!

Words: Dr Seuss
Music: Eugene Poddany

Once they know the tune, children will have fun substituting their own favourite "eats".

7 My ship sailed from China

1 My ship sailed from China
With a cargo of tea,
All laden with presents
For you and for me.
    They brought me a fan:
    Just imagine my bliss
    When I fan myself gaily
    Like this, like this, like this, like this.

2 My ship sailed from China . . . .
    They brought me a brush:
    Just imagine my bliss
    When I brush my hair briskly
    Like this . . .

3 My ship sailed from China . . .
    They brought me some shoes:
    Just imagine my bliss
    When I tap my feet lightly
    Like this . . .

Words and music: Traditional, with additional verses by June Witham

brought me a fan: Just im - a - gine my

C   Am   F

bliss   When I   fan   my - self   gai - ly   Like

G⁷   G⁷

this,   like   this,   like   this,   like   this.

C

The words chosen for this particular version allow for cumulative action, one hand only being used in the first verse for the fanning action, both hands being used in the second verse for simultaneous fanning and brushing, and foot tapping being added to the other actions in the third verse.

The children could well suggest verses of their own.

It might be pointed out that this song is in waltz time with three beats in each bar. Also, that it starts on an up-beat, with consequent reference to conductors and beating time.

8 Daisy Bell

Daisy, Daisy, give me your answer, do!
I'm half crazy, all for the love of you!
It won't be a stylish marriage,
I can't afford a carriage,
But you'll look sweet on the seat
Of a bicycle made for two!

CHIME BARS

Dai - sy, Dai - sy, give me your
F   Bb

ans - wer, do! _____ I'm half cra -
        F   C7   F

zy, all for the love of you! _____ It
Dm   Gm   C7

Words and music: Harry Dacre

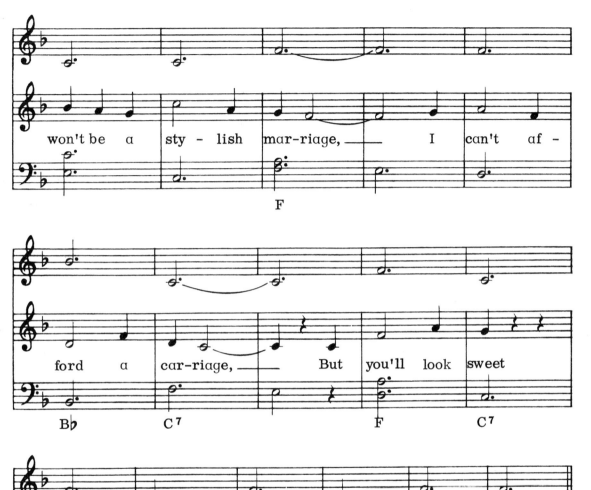

won't be a sty-lish mar-riage, ___ I can't af-

F

ford a car-riage, ___ But you'll look sweet

B♭ C⁷ F C⁷

on the seat of a bi-cy-cle made for two! ___

F C⁷ F C⁷ F

The part for chime bars uses only F, B♭ and C. In the key of F, these are doh, fah and soh – harmonically speaking, the three most important notes of the scale.

A bicycle bell could be used to pick out the last beat in each bar.

This song sounds very effective sung with chime bars and bicycle bell accompaniment alone.

9 The bonny blue-eyed sailor

1   Oh, there came to our village
    A bonny blue-eyed sailor,
    And he gave me a kiss
    And he went to sea,
    And the butcher, the baker,
    The cobbler and the tailor
    Oh, they all want to marry me.

2   Now the butcher has land,
    And the baker he has money,
    And the tailor has satin
    And corduroy,
    And the cobbler has bees
    And I'm very fond of honey,
    But I'll wait for my sailor boy.

3   I'll be mute as a mouse,
    I'll be quiet as a quaker
    Till his ship lies at anchor
    In Plymouth Bay;
    When the cobbler, the tailor,
    The butcher and the baker
    All shall dance on my wedding day.

Any one of the various bass line rhythms might be used as a repetitive theme for percussion accompaniment:

Any suitable traditional percussion instrument might be used or children might think of ways of suggesting the sounds they might hear on a ship at sea, such as a ship's bell, anchor chains, ropes creaking, waves lapping, seagulls crying.

Words: Rose Fyleman
Music: English folk tune, adapted by Thomas F. Dunhill

10 Old woman, old woman

1 Old woman, old woman,
Will you come a-shearing?
Speak a little louder, sir,
I'm very hard of hearing.

2 Old woman, old woman,
Will you come a-gleaning?
Speak a little louder, sir,
I cannot tell your meaning.

3 Old woman, old woman,
Will you come a-walking?
Speak a little louder, sir,
Or what's the use of talking?

4 Old woman, old woman,
Shall I love you dearly?
Thank you very kindly, sir,
I hear you very clearly!

DESCANT RECORDER OR GLOCKENSPIEL

1. Old wo-man, old wo-man, will you come a - shear - ing?

Speak a lit - tle loud-er, sir, I'm ve - ry hard of hear - ing.

The descant recorder part has much the same shape as the melody. It is helpful to sight reading to discuss the shapes of melodies with children, asking such questions as whether notes next to one another are on the same level, or whether they are just one note up or down, or whether there is a big jump. The children might be able to make graphs of tune shapes.

Words and music: Traditional

11 Li'l Liza Jane

1 I know a gal that you don't know,
    Li'l Liza Jane,
'Way down south in Baltimo',
    Li'l Liza Jane.

    Oh, Eliza, li'l Liza Jane,
    Oh, Eliza, li'l Liza Jane!

2 Liza Jane looks good to me,
    Li'l Liza Jane,
Sweetest one I ever see,
    Li'l Liza Jane.
    Oh, Eliza . . .

3 Where she lives the posies grow,
    Li'l Liza Jane,
Chickens roun' the kitchen do',
    Li'l Liza Jane.
    Oh, Eliza . . .

4 What do I care how far we roam?
    Li'l Liza Jane,
Where she's at is home, sweet home,
    Li'l Liza Jane.
    Oh, Eliza . . .

Words and music: Traditional American song

12 Clementine

1. In a cavern, in a canyon,
   Excavating for a mine,
   Dwelt a miner, forty niner,
   And his daughter Clementine.

   Oh my darling, oh my darling,
   Oh my darling Clementine!
   Thou art lost and gone forever,
   Dreadful sorry, Clementine.

2. Light she was and like a fairy,
   And her shoes were number nine,
   Herring boxes without topses
   Sandals were for Clementine.

3. Drove she ducklings to the water
   Every morning just at nine.
   Hit her foot against a splinter,
   Fell into the foaming brine.

4. Saw her lips above the water
   Blowing bubbles mighty fine,
   But alas! I was no swimmer,
   So I lost my Clementine.

5. How I missed her, how I missed her,
   How I missed my Clementine.
   But I kissed her little sister
   And forgot my Clementine.

Words and music: Traditional American song

13 Sparrow twitters

1 Sparrow twitters, "Cheep, cheep, cheep!
   Who will wed our chimney sweep?
   I know who his wife will be,
   Miller's daughter, Marjorie."

2 Sparrow chirrups in the birch,
   "Now they're coming from the church,
   Each and everyone is there
   Waiting for the bridal pair."

3 Sparrow warbles in the tree,
   "You shall see what you shall see,
   It will be a pretty fix,
   Soot and flour never mix!"

The descant recorder part to the two introductory bars is meant to suggest the twittering of a sparrow.

Words: C. K. Offer
Music: Czech folk tune, arranged by Vera Gray

14 Little brown jug

1   My wife and I lived all alone
       In a little log hut we called our own.
       She loved gin and I loved rum,
       I tell you what, we'd lots of fun.

       Ha, ha, ha, you and me,
       Little brown jug , don't I love thee,
       Ha, ha, ha, you and me,
       Little brown jug, don't I love thee!

2   The rose is red, my nose is too,
       The violet's blue and so are you.
       And yet I guess before I stop,
       I'd better have another drop.

A jazz theme has been used for the descant recorder part to the chorus.

Words and music: Traditional

15 I'm Henery the Eighth, I am

You don't know who you're looking at;
   now have a look at me!
I'm a bit of a nob, I am –
   belong to royaltee.
I'll tell you how it came about;
   I married Widow Burch,
And I was King of England
   when I toddled out of church.
Outside the people started shouting
   "Hip hooray!"
Said I, "Get down upon your knees,
   it's Coronation Day!"

   I'm Henery the Eighth, I am!
   Henery the Eighth, I am! I am!
   I got married to the widow next door,
   She's been married seven times before.
   Ev'ry one was a Henery –
   She wouldn't have a Willie or a Sam.
   I'm her eighth old man named Henery,
   I'm Henery the Eighth, I am.

Words and music: Murray and Weston

16 There's a hole in my bucket

1. There's a hole in my bucket, dear Liza, dear Liza,
   There's a hole in my bucket, dear Liza, a hole.

2. Then mend it, dear Georgie, dear Georgie, dear Georgie,
   Then mend it, dear Georgie, dear Georgie, mend it!

3. With what shall I mend it, dear Liza?

4. With a straw, dear Georgie . . . a straw!

5. The straw is too long, dear Liza.

6. Then cut it, dear Georgie . . . cut it!

7. With what shall I cut it, dear Liza?

8. With a knife, dear Georgie . . . a knife!

9. The knife is too blunt, dear Liza.

10. Then sharpen it, dear Georgie . . . sharpen it!

11. With what shall I sharpen it, dear Liza?

12. With a stone, dear Georgie . . . a stone!

13. The stone is too dry, dear Liza.

14. Then wet it, dear Georgie . . . wet it!

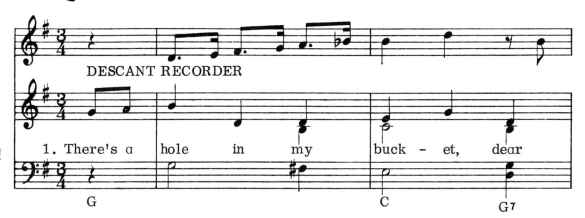

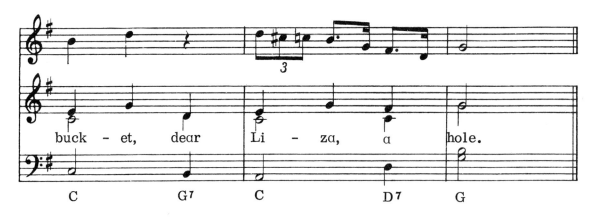

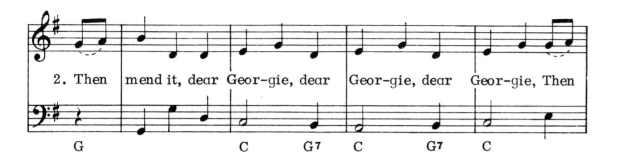

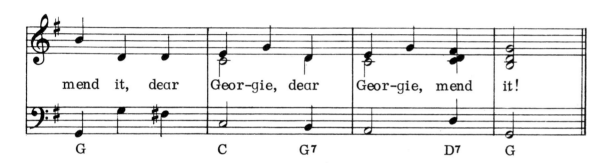

15 With what shall I wet it, dear Liza?

16 With water, dear Georgie . . . with water!

17 In what shall I get it, dear Liza?

18 In a bucket, dear Georgie . . . a bucket!

19 There's a hole in my bucket, dear Liza.

A different accompaniment is provided for alternate verses to provide variety. The jazz style descant recorder part can be used with either.

The class might be divided into two groups for this song, or even four or eight groups, allowing scope for individual performance.

Words and music: Traditional

17 There was an old witch

1 There was an old witch,
   Believe it if you can,
   She tapped on the window
   And she ran, ran, ran.
   She ran helter, skelter,
   With her toes in the air,
   Cornstalks flying
   From the old witch's hair.

2 "Swish," goes the broomstick,
   "Meow," goes the cat,
   "Plop", goes the hop-toad
   Sitting on her hat.
   "Wee," chuckled I,
   "What fun, fun, fun!"
   Hallowe'en night
   When the witches run.

Words and music: Traditional

18 Ten in the bed

1 There were ten in the bed
And the little one said,
"Roll over! Roll over!"
So they all rolled over and one fell out.

2 There were nine in the bed . . .

3 There were eight in the bed . . .

4 There were seven in the bed . . .

5 There were six in the bed . . .

6 There were five in the bed . . .

7 There were four in the bed . . .

8 There were three in the bed . . .

9 There were two in the bed . . .

10 There was one in the bed
And this little one said,
"Good night! Good night!"

1. There were ten in the bed And the lit-tle one said, "Roll o-ver! Roll

G (throughout)

Fine

D.S. al Fine

o-ver!" So they all rolled o-ver and one fell out. There were

The following percussion accompaniment is suggested for the first four bars, keeping a steady rhythm on chime bar B:

Words and music: Traditional English

19 Lily the pink

We'll drink a drink, a drink
To Lily the pink, the pink, the pink,
The saviour of the human race.
For she invented
Medicinal compound,
Most efficacious in every case.

1 Mister Flears had sticking-out ears,
   And it made him awful shy.
   And so they gave him
   Medicinal compound;
   Now he's learning how to fly.

2 Brother Tony was known to be bony,
   He would never eat his meals.
   And so they gave him
   Medicinal compound;
   Now they move him round on wheels.

3 Johnny Hammer had a terrible s. s. stammer,
   He could hardly say a w. word.
   And so they gave him
   Medicinal compound;
   Now he's seen, but never heard.

Words and music: Adapted and arranged by Gorman, McGear and McCough

One suggestion for a simple chime bar accompaniment is to strike one note on the first beat of each bar, using the sequence

C C G G G G C C

throughout.

Further percussion accompaniment might be added by tapping a drinking glass or a jar filled with water to the rhythm

throughout the chorus.

20 Bananas in pyjamas

Bananas,
In pyjamas,
Are coming down the stairs;
Bananas,
In pyjamas,
Are coming down in pairs;
Bananas,
In pyjamas,
Are chasing teddy bears –
'Cos on Tuesdays
They all try to
CATCH THEM UNAWARES.

Words and music: Carey Blyton

cha - sing ted-dy bears -   'Cos   on Tues-days They all try to

G⁷

1st time   **Repeat ad lib**   **Last time**

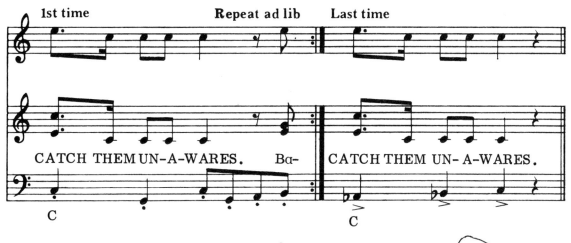

CATCH THEM UN-A-WARES.   Ba-   CATCH THEM UN-A-WARES.

C   C

The rhythm of the introduction

can be kept up throughout by drums.

Maracas might be used to follow the rhythm of the melody. A more unconventional type of shaker might be made out of papier maché, using a real banana as a mould shape.

When making papier maché instruments, it helps to give strength and resonance to the finished instrument if fine material is used for one of the layers in place of paper.

21 I know an old lady

1 I know an old lady who swallowed a fly.
I don't know why she swallowed a fly.
I guess she'll die.

2 I know an old lady who swallowed a spider,
That wriggled and jiggled and tickled inside her.
She swallowed the spider to catch the fly,
I don't know why she swallowed a fly.
I guess she'll die.

3 I know an old lady who swallowed a bird.
How absurd to swallow a bird!
She swallowed the bird to catch the spider
That wriggled and jiggled and tickled inside her.
She swallowed the spider to catch the fly,
I don't know why she swallowed a fly.
I guess she'll die.

4 I know an old lady who swallowed a cat.
Imagine that! She swallowed a cat.
She swallowed the cat to catch the bird . . .

5 I know an old lady who swallowed a dog.
What a hog to swallow a dog!
She swallowed the dog to catch the cat . . .

6 I know an old lady who swallowed a goat.
Opened her throat and swallowed a goat.
She swallowed the goat to catch the dog . . .

Verses 3-7

3. I know an old la-dy who swal-lowed a bird. How absurd to swal-low a bird!

F   Gm   C7

Repeat this section as needed

She swallowed the bird to catch the spider That wrig-gled and jig-gled and

F   Gm

tick-led in - side her.   She swal-lowed the spi - der to

C7   F

catch the fly, I don't know why she swal-lowed a fly. I guess she'll

Gm   C7

al 𝄋 Last verse   **Spoken**

die. I know an old la-dy who swal-lowed a horse. She's dead, of course!

F   F   C7   F

7 I know an old lady who swallowed a cow.
   I don't know how she swallowed a cow.
   She swallowed a cow to catch the goat . . .

8 I know an old lady who swallowed a horse.
   She's dead, of course!

Words and music: _____
Rose Bonne and Alan Mills

22 Michael Finnigin

1. There was an old man called Michael Finnigin,
He grew whiskers on his chinigin,
The wind came up and blew them inigin,
    Poor old Michael Finnigin. Beginigin!

2. There was an old man called Michael Finnigin,
He kicked up an awful dinigin,
Because they said he must not singigin,
    Poor old Michael Finnigin. Beginigin!

3. There was an old man called Michael Finnigin,
He went fishing with a pinigin,
Caught a fish but dropped it inigin,
    Poor old Michael Finnigin. Beginigin!

4. There was an old man called Michael Finnigin,
Climbed a tree and barked his shinigin,
Took off several yards of skinigin,
    Poor old Michael Finnigin. Beginigin!

5. There was an old man called Michael Finnigin,
He grew fat and then grew thinigin,
Then he died and had to beginigin,
    Poor old Michael Finnigin, STOP!

This tune could be accompanied by chime bars alone, using F and C only in the following sequence, one beat per bar:

F F C C F F C F

Words and music: Traditional

23 The train is a-coming

1 The train is a-coming, oh yes,
Train is a-coming, oh yes,
Train is a-coming, train is a-coming,
Train is a-coming, oh yes.

2 You'd better get your ticket, oh yes,
Better get your ticket, oh yes,
Better get your ticket, better get your ticket,
Better get your ticket, oh yes.

3 There's room for a few more, oh yes

4 The train is a-leaving, oh yes

5 We're going to the seaside, oh yes

6 We've got to go home now, oh yes

A train sound might be made by means of a soft whistle, an ocarina, or the voice using the sounds "oo oo". These sounds would be effective limited to the second, fourth and eighth bars on the off-beats, that is, on the second and fourth beats.

Another suggested percussion accompaniment is castanets playing the following steady rhythm throughout:

Words and music: Traditional American, with additional verses

24 Wheels keep turning

Some machines are fun to watch
And make a funny sound;
With some oil on, they go quieter,
That's what I have found.
Up and down the levers go,
Pistons to and fro.
Motors churning,
Brrrm, Brrrm
Wheels keep turning,
Brrrm, Brrrm
Round and round and round and round
And round and round and round.

Words and music: Graham Beebee

Pis-tons to and fro. Mo-tors churn-ing, Brrrm, Brrrm

G7 C G7 C G7

Wheels keep turn - ing, Brrrm, Brrrm Round and round and

C G7 C G7 C G7

round and round And round and round and round. (Piano only)

C G7 C G7 C

As well as the traditional percussion instruments suggested here, use might be made of a football crake or of pebbles in a can. Children could discuss where these might be used most effectively.

25 Morningtown ride

1. Train whistle blowin',
   Makes a sleepy noise;
   Underneath their blankets
   Go all the girls and boys.

   Rockin', rollin', ridin',
   Out along the bay,
   All bound for Morningtown,
   Many miles away.

2. Driver at the engine,
   Fireman rings the bell;
   Sandman swings the lantern
   To say that all is well.

3. Maybe it is raining
   Where our train will ride;
   All the little travellers
   Are warm and snug inside.

4. Somewhere there is sunshine,
   Somewhere there is day;
   Somewhere there is Morningtown,
   Many miles away.

Words and music: Malvina Reynolds

The suggested part for descant recorder is difficult, but it is great fun for advanced players.

26 She'll be coming round the mountain

1   She'll be coming round the mountain
        when she comes,
    She'll be coming round the mountain
        when she comes,
    She'll be coming round the mountain,
        coming round the mountain,
    Coming round the mountain when she comes.

2   She'll be driving six white horses
        when she comes . . .

3   Oh, we'll all go out and meet her
        when she comes . . .

4   Oh, we'll kill the old red rooster
        when she comes . . .

5   And we'll all have chicken and dumplings
        when she comes . . .

6   Oh, she'll have to sleep with grandma
        when she comes . . .

7   She'll be wearing pink pyjamas
        when she comes . . .

Words and music: Traditional American

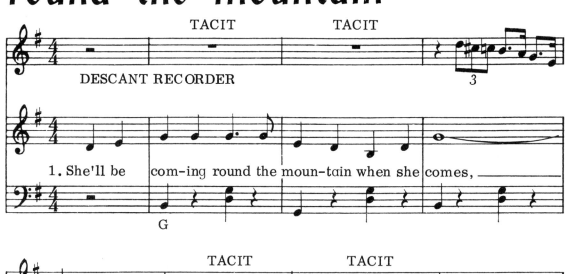

DESCANT RECORDER

1. She'll be com-ing round the moun-tain when she comes, ____

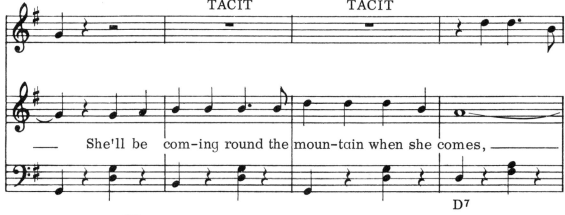

____ She'll be com-ing round the moun-tain when she comes, ____

The musical term "triplet" – three notes played in the time allowed for two – might be introduced in connection with the descant recorder part.

27 The Wombling Song

1 Underground, overground, Wombling free,
   The Wombles of Wimbledon Common are we,
   Making good use of the things that we find,
   Things that the everyday folks leave behind.
      Uncle Bulgaria he can remember the days
      When he wasn't behind "The Times"
      With his map of the world
      Pick up the papers and take 'em to Tobermory.
   Wombles are organised, work as a team,
   Wombles are tidy and Wombles are clean;
   Overground, underground, Wombling free,
   The Wombles of Wimbledon Common are we.

2 People don't notice us, they never see
   Under their noses a Womble may be;
   We Womble by night and Womble by day,
   Looking for litter to trundle away.
      We're so incredibly, utterly devious,
      Making the most of everything,
      Even bottles and tins;
      Pick up the pieces and mak'em into something
      new.
   Underground, overground, Wombling free,
   The Wombles of Wimbledon Common are we,
   Making good use of the things that we find,
   Things that the everyday folks leave behind.

Words and music: Mike Batt

The very high notes in bars 15 to 18 might be sung an octave lower.

All sheet music for Wombling Songs is available from Chappell & Co Ltd, 50 New Bond Street, London W1

28 Shoot! Shoot! Shoot!

The ball is at my feet,
I swerve and beat a man;
I'm haring down the touchline,
Just catch me if you can.
I dodge a sliding tackle,
The centre-half is near,
And all at once I hear the crowd
And this is what I hear:

Fifty thousand football fans
Shout, "Shoot! Shoot! Shoot!"
From all around the football ground,
It's "Shoot! Shoot! Shoot!"
From thirty yards
Then I get set,
I kick the ball
Straight in the net.
I hear a roar I can't forget,
It's "Goal! Goal! Goal!
It's a goal, goal, goal!"

Words and music: Peter Canwell

Chorus

Fif - ty thou - sand foot - ball fans Shout, "Shoot! Shoot! Shoot!" From

C   F   G7

all a - round the foot - ball ground, It's "Shoot! Shoot! Shoot!" From

C   G   D7   G7

thir - ty yards Then I get set, I kick the ball Straight in the net. I

F   C

hear the roar I can't for-get, It's "Goal! Goal! Goal! It's a goal, goal, goal!"

F   Dm   G7   Am   F   G7   C

Percussion accompaniment might be provided by a drum beating four beats in every bar.

A football crake might be used in bars 2, 4, 8 and 9 of the chorus.

D

29 Battle song of the Zartians

1 Calling all Zartians to take a stand.
   Earthman invaders approach our land.
   Up and attack to make them draw back,
   We are all set and our space-ships manned.

2 Though we are small, we are bold and strong,
   Our two antennae are extra long:
   They can detect each thought as you think it,
   They can transmit every Zartian song.

3 We are the masters of all the sky,
   Out into space let our rockets fly.
   As you come nearer into our orbit,
   Two-legged strangers, prepare to die!

The descant recorder part mainly follows the bass line. The children might be interested in finding out where the two parts deviate and this could offer a valuable exercise in transposing from the bass to the treble clef.

Words: Jenyth Worsley
Music: Canadian melody

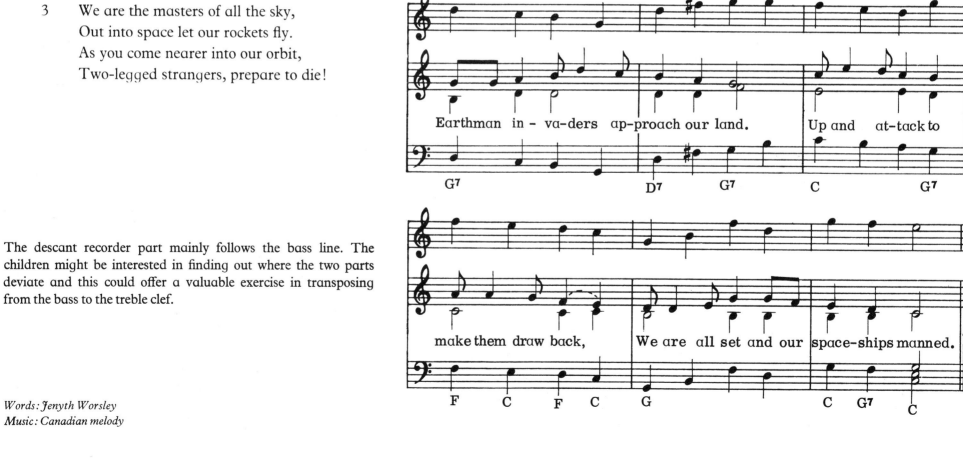

30 The wind blow east

1   Oh, the wind blow east,
    The wind blow west,
    The wind blow the *Sunshine*
    Right down in town.

        Oh, the wind blow the *Sunshine*
        Right down in town,
        Oh, the wind blow the *Sunshine*
        Right down in town.

2   Oh, the wind blow east,
    The wind blow west,
    The wind blow the *Setting Star*
    Right down in town.

        Oh, the wind blow the *Setting Star*
        Right down in town,
        Oh, the wind blow the *Setting Star*
        Right down in town.

Sunshine and *Setting Star* are the names of two ships. They were blown right down in town by a hurricane in the Bahamas.

Children will enjoy suggesting other things which may be blown down in town by the wind, e.g. autumn leaves.

The recorder players could try holding the note D throughout the chorus, taking breaths as necessary.

Words and music: from Nassau, Bahamas

DESCANT RECORDER OR GLOCKENSPIEL

1. Oh, the wind blow east, The wind blow west,

The wind blow the Sun-shine Right down in town.

Chorus (Repeat many times without stopping)

Oh, the wind blow the Sun-shine Right down in town,

Oh, the wind blow the Sun-shine Right down in town.

31 One potato, two potato

1 In my little garden – now promise you won't laugh –
I haven't any flowers and I haven't any grass,
But now I'm going to dig and plant
And soon I'll have a show;
With a bit of sun and a bit of rain
There'll be a lovely row of

    One potato, two potato, three potato, four,
    Five potato, six potato, seven potato, more.
    One potato, two potato, three potato, four,
    Five potato, six potato, seven potato, more.

2 I'm going to grow so many things, I'll surely
    never starve,
Cabbages and cauliflowers, I won't do things
    by halves,
I'll plant a row of runner beans,
They'll grow so very high,
With a bit of sun and a bit of rain,
They'll reach up to the sky.

3 So if you're ever down my way, do please
    drop in for tea.
We'll have lettuces and radishes, they'll all be
    grown by me,
Tomatoes, too, and cucumbers,
Oh, what a lovely spread!
And if you do not like that,
You can always have instead:

Words: Peter Charlton
Music: Paul Reade

Chorus

One po-ta-to, two po-ta-to, three po-ta-to, four, Five po-ta-to, six po-ta-to,

F   G7   C7

se-ven po-ta-to, more.   One po-ta-to, two po-ta-to,

F   C7   F

three pota-to, four,   Five pota-to, six pota-to, seven pota-to, more.

G7   C7   F

The descant recorder part provides a good exercise in tonguing. It is suggested that the children begin by saying t t t as in po*ta*to.

32 The guard song

We're the guard by the palace gate,
Keeping watch at our posts night and day;
We're the guard standing tall and straight
And the people must do as we say.
When a stranger comes that we do not know,
You can hear our voices ring:
"Who goes there? Are you friend or foe?
Then pass in the name of the Queen."

Words and music: Molly Mason James

DESCANT RECORDER

We're the guard by the pa - lace gate, Keep-ing
watch at our posts night and day; We're the guard standing
tall and straight, And the peo - ple must do as we say. When a

The descant recorder part suggests a bugle call, with its triplets and limited range of notes. This part uses only the three notes of the major triad, F A C in key of F, or doh, me, soh.

The jazz band kazoo is fun to use for this part and helps children to realise how difficult it is to make notes for themselves and keep in perfect pitch with the other players and singers.

stran - ger comes that we do not know, You can

hear our voi - ces ring: "Who goes there? Are you

friend or foe? Then pass in the name of the Queen."

33 The fireman

With his helmet and his axe
And his ladder and his hose,
Every fireman fights the fire
As everybody knows.
He's a man who's very brave
And he's got to climb up high,
Hosing water on the flames
As they leap into the sky.

When they hear the fire-bell,
Down the pole they zoom
On to the red engine,
Boom! Boom! Boom!
Standing on the engine,
The men we all admire,
Those fighting men, the firemen,
They're going to fight the fire.

Words: Ken Blakeson
Music: Peter Canwell

34 When Father papered the parlour *Chorus only.*

1   Our parlour wanted papering,
      and Pa said it was waste
To call a paperhanger in,
      and so he made some paste.
He bought some rolls of paper,
      got a ladder and a brush,
And with my Mummy's nightgown on
      at it he made a rush.

     When Father papered the parlour,
     You couldn't see him for paste!
     Dabbing it here, dabbing it there,
     Paste and paper everywhere.
     Mother was stuck to the ceiling,
     The children stuck to the floor,
     I never knew a blooming family
     So "stuck up" before.

2   We're never going to move away
      from that house any more,
For Father's gone and stuck the chairs
      and table to the floor.
We can't find our piano,
      though it's broad and rather tall,
We think that it's behind the paper
      Pa stuck on the wall.

Words and music: Weston and Barnes

Chorus

When Fa-ther papered the par-lour, You could-n't see him for paste!__

Dm   Gm   Dm

Dab-bing it here,   dab-bing it there,   Paste and pa-per ev-ery-where.

A⁷   Dm   A

Moth-er was stuck to the ceil - ing, The child-ren stuck to the floor,__ I

Dm   B♭   A

ne - ver knew a bloom-ing fa-mi-ly So "stuck up" be-fore.

Dm   C   F   Gm⁷   A⁷   Dm

35 The clown

1 When the circus comes to town,
   I love to see the clown
   Racing round the great Big Top,
   His trousers falling down.
   A very jolly person
   Who makes me laugh and shout.
   I always feel so happy
   When the funny clown's about.

       Ha ha ha ha
       Ha ha ha ha
       Oh oh oh oh oh,
       Ha ha ha ha
       Ha ha ha,
       The funny circus clown.

2 Wearing baggy trousers
   And a very floppy hat,
   See his boots, they're far too big,
   He trips up on the mat.
   A very jolly person
   Who makes me laugh and shout.
   I always feel so happy
   When the funny clown's about.

Words: Ken Blakeson
Music: Peter Canwell

al-ways feel so hap-py When the | fun-ny clown's about.

D7   G

Chorus

Ha ha ha ha Ha ha ha ha | Oh oh oh oh oh,

G   D7

Ha ha ha ha Ha ha ha, The | fun-ny cir-cus clown.

G

This song may be sung starting with the chorus.

The part for chime bars is very simple to play. When playing the notes of the chorus, it is suggested that children beat as fast as they can for the correct duration of each note.

36 Song of the Delhi Tongawallah

Gallop quickly, gallop quickly,
Gallop quickly, brother horse.
Gallop quickly, gallop quickly,
Gallop quickly, brother horse.

1   We have still five miles of travelling
    And the shades of night are falling.
        Gallop quickly . . .

2   If cruel robbers do waylay us,
    What to do then? What to do then?
        Gallop quickly . . .

3   Grain and grass be yours in plenty
    If we get home quickly, horse.
        Gallop quickly . . .

The Delhi Tongawallah is a ponycart driver.

The part for chime bars uses only D, G and A. In the key of D, these are doh, fah and soh – the three most important notes of the scale in traditional harmony.

Words: English version by Getsie Samuel
Music: Hindustani folk song

37 Rabbit ain't got

1. Rabbit ain't got no tail at all,
   Tail at all, tail at all,
   Rabbit ain't got no tail at all,
   Just a powder puff.

2. Rabbit don't wear no cutaway coat,
   Cutaway coat, cutaway coat,
   Rabbit don't wear no cutaway coat,
   Just a suit of fur.

3. Rabbit don't eat no bacon and egg,
   Bacon and egg, bacon and egg,
   Rabbit don't eat no bacon and egg,
   Just a field of grass.

4. Rabbit don't need no pots and pans,
   Pots and pans, pots and pans,
   Rabbit don't need no pots and pans,
   Just a set of teeth.

5. Rabbit don't have no motor car,
   Motor car, motor car,
   Rabbit don't have no motor car,
   Just his own four legs.

6. Rabbit don't have to build no house,
   Build no house, build no house,
   Rabbit don't have to build no house,
   Just a deep dark hole.

DESCANT RECORDER OR SECOND VOICE

The children might be able to hear that the recorder part follows the melody a third above, except for two notes, and to pick out these notes.

Words and music: Traditional, with additional verses by Margaret Baker

38 The animals went in two by two

1 The animals went in two by two,
    Hurrah! Hurrah!
The animals went in two by two,
    Hurrah! Hurrah!
The animals went in two by two,
The elephant and the kangaroo,
    And they all went into the ark
    For to get out of the rain.

2 The animals went in three by three . . .
The wasp, the ant and the bumble bee . . .

3 The animals went in four by four . . .
The great hippopotamus stuck in the door . . .

4 The animals went in five by five . . .
By eating each other they kept alive . . .

5 The animals went in six by six . . .
They turned out the monkey because of his
    tricks . . .

6 The animals went in seven by seven . . .
The little pig thought he was going to
    heaven . . .

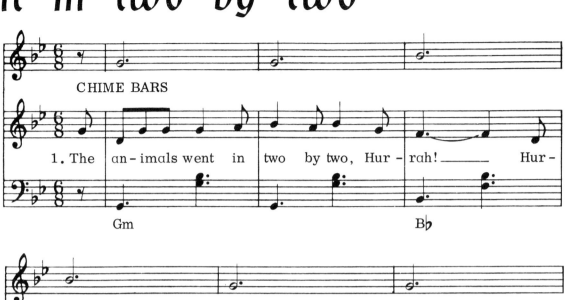

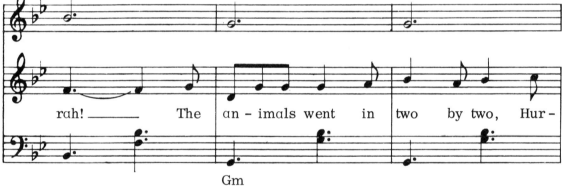

Words and music: Traditional

39 Going to the zoo

1   Daddy's taking us to the zoo tomorrow,
     zoo tomorrow, zoo tomorrow,
  Daddy's taking us to the zoo tomorrow,
  We can stay all day.

    We're going to the zoo, zoo, zoo.
    How about you, you, you?
    You can come too, too, too,
    We're going to the zoo, zoo, zoo.

2   See the elephant with the long trunk swinging',
  Great big ears and long trunk swingin',
  Sniffing up peanuts with the long trunk swingin',
  We can stay all day.

3   See all the monkeys scritch, scritch scratchin',
  Jumpin' all around and scritch, scritch
    scratchin',
  Hangin' by their long tails, scritch, scritch
    scratchin',
  We can stay all day.

4   Big black bear all huff huff a-puffin',
  Coat's too heavy, he's huff huff a-puffin',
  Don't get near the huff huff a-puffin'
  Or you won't stay all day.

Words and music: Tom Paxton

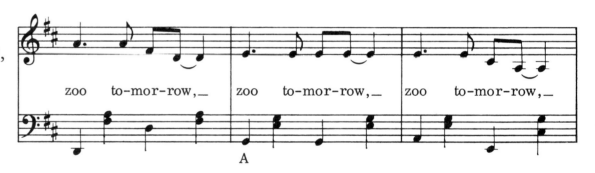

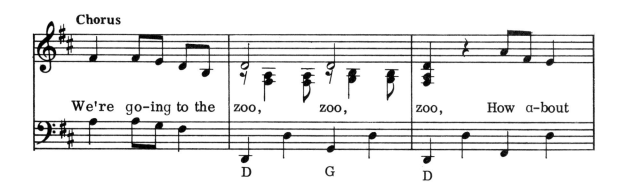

Chorus

We're go-ing to the zoo, zoo, zoo, How a-bout

D   G   D

you, you, you? You can come too, too,

G   D   Am

Last verse

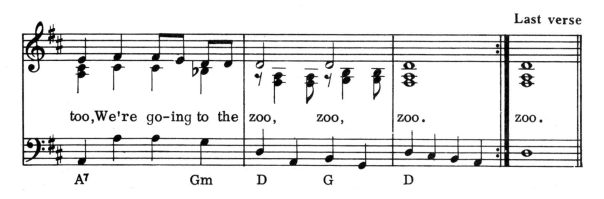

too, We're go-ing to the zoo, zoo, zoo. zoo.

A⁷   Gm   D   G   D

40 The hippopotamus song

1 A bold hippopotamus was standing one day
   On the banks of the cool Shalimar.
   He gazed at the bottom as it peacefully lay
   By the light of the evening star.
   Away on the hilltop sat combing her hair,
   His fair Hippopotamine maid.
   The hippopotamus was no ignoramus
   And sang her this sweet serenade.

        Mud, mud, glorious mud!
        Nothing quite like it for cooling the blood.
        So follow me, follow, down to the hollow,
        And there let us wallow in glorious mud.

2 The fair hippopotamus he aimed to entice
   From her seat on the hill top above,
   As she hadn't got a Ma to give her advice
   Came tiptoeing down to her love.
   Like thunder the forest re-echoed the sound
   Of the song that they sang as they met.
   His inamorata adjusted her garter
   And lifted her voice in duet.

ta-mus was no ig-nor-amus And sang her this sweet sere-nade:

F7   C7   F   Cm   C7   F

Chorus

Mud, mud, glor-i-ous mud! No-thing quite like it for

Bb   F7   Bb   C7

cool-ing the blood. So fol-low me, fol-low, down to the hol-low, And

F7   Bb   Cm

there let us wal-low in glor - i-ous mud.

Eb   Bb   F   Bb

3   Now more hippopotami began to convene
On the banks of that river so wide.
I wonder what am I to say of the scene
That ensued by the Shalimar side.
They dived all at once with an ear-splitting splosh,
Then rose to the surface again,
A regular army of hippopotami
All singing this haunting refrain.

Words: Michael Flanders
Music: Donald Swann and Michael Flanders

41 Tiger, tiger

Tiger, tiger, orange and black,
He's somewhere about
   so you'd better watch out!
Tiger, tiger, orange and black,
There on the ground,
   I can see your tracks.
So tiger, tiger, orange and black,
I'm going home in case you jump
   on my back!

Words and music: Peter Canwell

42 Where, oh where has my little dog gone?

1 Where, oh where has my little dog gone?
Oh, where, oh, where can he be?
With his tail cut short and his ears cut long,
Oh, where, oh, where can he be?

2 My little dog always waggles his tail
Whenever he wants his grog.
And if the tail were more strong than he,
Why, the tail would waggle the dog.

Words and music: Traditional American

43 Daddy wouldn't buy me a bow-wow

I love my little cat, I do,
Its coat is oh so warm,
It comes each day with me to school
And sits upon the form.
When teacher says, "Why do you bring
That little pet of yours?"
I tell her that I bring my cat
Along with me because –

Daddy wouldn't buy me a bow-wow (bow-wow),
Daddy wouldn't buy me a bow-wow (bow-wow),
I've got a little cat,
I am very fond of that,
But I'd rather have a bow-wow, wow-wow,
 wow-wow,
Daddy wouldn't buy me a bow-wow (bow-wow),
Daddy wouldn't buy me a bow-wow (bow-wow),
I've got a little cat,
I am very fond of that,
But I'd rather have a bow-wow-wow.

Words and music: Joseph Tabrar

Chorus

Dad-dy wouldn't buy me a bow-wow (bow-wow), Daddy wouldn't buy me a

C   G7   C

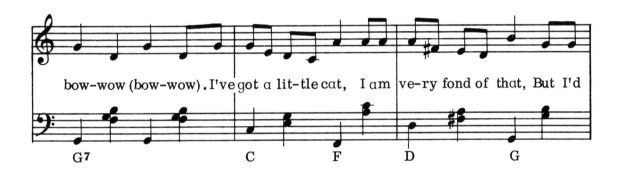

bow-wow (bow-wow). I've got a lit-tle cat, I am ve-ry fond of that, But I'd

G7   C   F   D   G

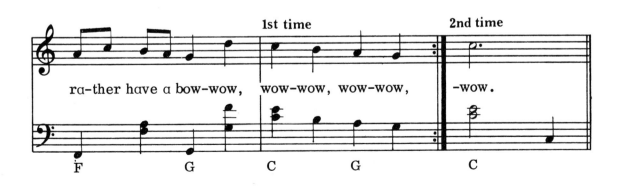

1st time   2nd time

ra-ther have a bow-wow,   wow-wow, wow-wow,   -wow.

F   G   C   G   C

44 Five little frogs

1 Five little speckled frogs
  Sat on a speckled log,
  Catching some most delicious bugs,
    yum, yum.
  One jumped into the pool,
  Where it was nice and cool,
  And there were four green speckled frogs,
    glub, glub.

2 Four little speckled frogs . . .

3 Three little speckled frogs . . .

4 Two little speckled frogs . . .

5 One little speckled frog
  Sat on a speckled log,
  Catching some most delicious bugs,
    yum, yum.
  He jumped into the pool
  Where it was nice and cool,
  And there were no green speckled frogs,
    glub, glub.

The descant recorder part given here might be nicknamed "the frog rock".

Words and music: Virginia Pavelko and L. B. Scott

45 Frog went a-courtin'

1 Frog went a-courtin' and he did ride,
  A-hum, a-hum,
  Frog went a-courtin' and he did ride,
  A-hum, a-hum,
  Frog went a-courtin' and he did ride,
  Sword and pistol by his side,
  A-hum, a-hum.

2 Rode right up to Miss Mouse's door,
  A-hum, a-hum,
  Rode right up to Miss Mouse's door,
  A-hum, a-hum,
  Rode right up to Miss Mouse's door,
  Gave three raps and a very loud roar,
  A-hum, a-hum.

3 Took Miss Mouse upon his knee,
  Said, "Miss Mouse, will you marry me?"

4 "Where shall the wedding supper be?"
  "Down in the swamp in the hollow tree."

5 "What shall the wedding supper be?"
  "Fried mosquito and a black-eyed pea."

A jazz type recorder part is suggested for this song.

Words and music: Traditional American

46 Down in Demerara

1 There was a man who had a horselum,
   Had a horselum, had a horselum,
   Was a man who had a horselum,
   Down in Demerara.

    And here we sits like birds in the wilderness,
    Birds in the wilderness, birds in the wilderness,
    Here we sits like birds in the wilderness,
    Down in Demerara.

2 Now that poor horse he broke his legalum,
   Broke his legalum, broke his legalum,
   That poor horse he broke his legalum,
   Down in Demerara.

3 Now that poor man he sent for a doctorum,
   Sent for a doctorum, sent for a doctorum,
   That poor man he sent for a doctorum,
   Down in Demerara.

4 Now that poor horse he went and diedalum,
   Went and diedalum, went and diedalum,
   That poor horse he went and diedalum,
   Down in Demerara.

5 And here we sits and flaps our wingsalum,
   Flaps our wingsalum, flaps our wingsalum,
   Here we sits and flaps our wingsalum,
   Down in Demerara.

Words and music: British student song

Chorus

And here we sits like birds in the wil-der-ness,

F

The descant recorder part is meant to suggest the continuous motion of the wings of birds in flight. It may be repeated for the chorus.

The word *arpeggio* might be introduced in connection with this part.

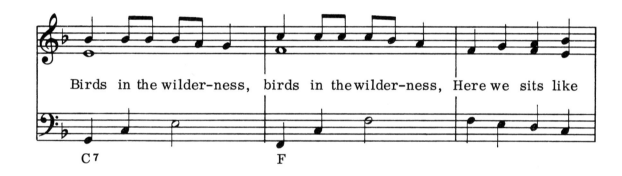

Birds in the wilder-ness, birds in thewilder-ness, Here we sits like

C 7   F

birds in thewilder-ness, Down in De-me- ra - ra.

C 7   F

47 The bear went over the mountain

The bear went over the mountain,
The bear went over the mountain,
The bear went over the mountain
To see what he could see.
And all that he could see,
And all that he could see,
Was the other side of the mountain,
The other side of the mountain,
The other side of the mountain
Was all that he could see.

Words and music: Traditional

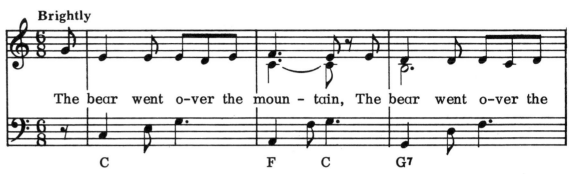

The bear went o-ver the moun - tain, The bear went o-ver the

moun - tain, The bear went o-ver the moun - tain To

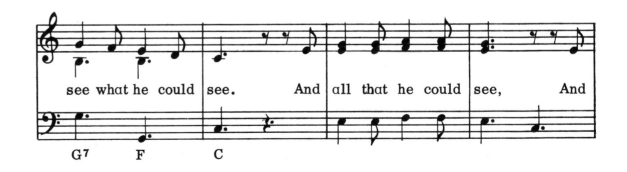

see what he could see. And all that he could see, And

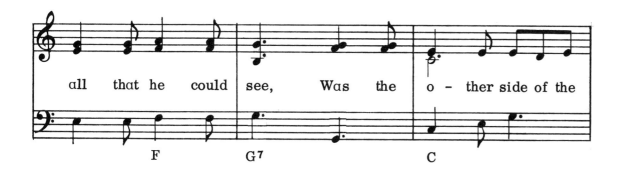

all that he could see, Was the o - ther side of the

F G7 C

moun - tain, The o - ther side of the moun - tain, The

F C G7 C

The children will enjoy suggesting other animals to go "over the mountain".

o - ther side of the moun - tain Was all that he could see.

F G7 C

48 Ferdinando, the donkey

1. "Get along, you lazy Ferdinando,
   We must leave the shade of the olive tree.
   Take me home at once; they'll be angry with me,
   Oh, take me home at once; they'll be angry
      with me!"
         Ee-aw, Ee-aw!
         Ee-aw, Ee-aw!

2. "Come along, my dearest Ferdinando,
   I've some lovely hay for you for tea.
   Leave those prickly thorns and come home with me,
   Oh, leave those prickly thorns and come home
      with me!"
         Ee-aw, Ee-aw!
         Ee-aw, Ee-aw!

3. If you have a donkey Ferdinando,
   Never let him stray by the olive tree.
   You will never get him home for tea,
   Oh, you will never get him home for tea!
         Ee-aw, Ee-aw!
         Ee-aw, Ee-aw!

Coconut shells might be used to follow one of the two rhythms in
the bass line:

or quavers might be played throughout.

Words: Jenyth Worsley
Music: Spanish traditional melody

49 The kangaroo song

I'm a kangaroo and I
Can jump so high
I touch the sky,
And all day long
I skip along
And sing my little song.

Hoppity, hoppity,
Skippity, skippity,
Jumpity jump
To the kangaroo song.
Hoppity, hoppity,
Skippity, skippity,
Jumpity jump
To the kangaroo song.

Words and music: Peter Canwell

50 Katie's garden

1 Katie was a kangaroo,
She made a lovely bride;
Her husband felt so happy
As she hopped off by his side.

   Katie, Katie kangaroo,
   As she hopped off by his side.

2 He took her to the little home
He'd lovingly prepared;
But Katie did not like it –
"There's no garden," she declared.

   Katie, Katie kangaroo,
   "There's no garden," she declared.

3 Her husband was resourceful,
He knew just what to do;
He filled her pouch with compost,
And bought some pansies too.

   Katie, Katie kangaroo,
   He bought some pansies too.

4 So now she has a garden,
   A very special kind;
   She always takes it with her,
   It's never left behind.

      Katie, Katie kangaroo,
      It's never left behind.

5 It tickles when she's weeding,
   And watering's not too good,
   But she prefers her garden tub
   To one that's made of wood.

      Katie, we like what you do,
      You're a clever kangaroo.

Children will enjoy illustrating this song.

Words: Rosamond Green
Music: G. C. Westcott

51 Apusski dusky

1   In middle ocean,
    Sardines are swimming,
        Apusski dusky, apusskidu.
    A boat sails over,
    Down comes a net.
        Apusski dusky, apusskidu.

2   One wise old sardine
    Flicks out a warning,
        Apusski dusky, apusskidu.
    Swift through the water
    They dart away.
        Apusski dusky, apusskidu.

3   With tails a-flashing,
    Sardines are swimming,
        Apusski dusky, apusskidu.
    So full of joy that
    They're swimming free.
        Apusski dusky, apusskidu.

Words and music: Traditional, with additional verses

CHIME BARS

2. One wise old sar - dine Flicks out a warn - ing, A-puss-ki

C   G7

dus - ky, a-puss-ki - du. Swift through the wa-ter They dart a-

C   C

way. A-puss-ki dus - ky, a-puss-ki - du.

F   G7   C

Two piano accompaniments are provided for this simple melody to add variety to alternate verses, or, of course, one accompaniment may be chosen in preference to the other.

The descant recorder and chime bar parts can be played either individually or together.

The alto line (the lower notes of the treble clef accompaniment) of the second version may be used an octave higher as an alternative descant recorder part.

52 The elephant

1   I'm a big grey lump
    And I thump, thump, thump
    Through the jungle, hot and green;
    With my long white tusks
    And my great big trunk,
    I'm the biggest thing you've seen.

    Thump! Thump! Thump!
    Trumpety trump,
    An elephant am I.
    I'm the biggest living animal
    Under the jungle sky.
    I thump, thump, thump,
    Trumpety trump,
    An elephant am I;
    I thump, thump, thump,
    Trumpety trump,
    An elephant am I.

2   See me suck the cool water
    Up my trunk,
    See me squirt it over me.
    With my big long trunk
    I can reach quite high,
    Eat bananas off a tree.

Words: Ken Blakeson
Music: Peter Canwell

53 Gobbolino, the witch's cat

1   One fine night in a witch's cavern
    Two little kittens rolled on to the floor;
    One, called Sootica, was black all over:
    The other, Gobbolino, had one white paw.

        Who'll give a home to a kitten?
        Who'll give a home to a cat?
        Gobbolino you may call me;
        I want just a fire and a mat.

2   One white paw and a sheen of tabby,
    Two lovely eyes, not green, but blue.
    None of the witches would take this kitten . . .
    And neither did his mother know what to do.

3   Then one day, when the sun was shining,
    Gobbolino found he was all alone.
    The witch had gone and deserted him for ever,
    So Gobbolino washed himself, then *he* left home.

Words and music: G. C. Westcott

The inspiration for this song was the story *Gobbolino: The Witch's Cat* by Ursula Moray Williams, published in the Young Puffin series. It is suggested that children make up their own verses to continue the story.

This song offers an excellent opportunity to point the contrast between off-beat stress and on-beat stress.

54 A windmill in old Amsterdam

1 A mouse lived in a windmill in old Amsterdam,
A windmill with a mouse in and he wasn't
   grousing.
He sang every morning, "How lucky I am
Living in a windmill in old Amsterdam!"

   I saw a mouse. Where?
   There on a stair.
   Where on a stair?
   Right there, a little mouse with clogs on,
   Well, I declare,
   Going clip clippety clop on the stair.

2 The mouse he got lonesome, he took him a wife;
A windmill with mice in is hardly surprising,
She sang every morning, "How lucky I am
Living in a windmill in old Amsterdam!"

3 First they had triplets and then they had quins,
A windmill with quins in, triplets and twins in.
They sang every morning, "How lucky we are
Living in a windmill in Amsterdam, ya!"

Words and music: Ted Dicks and Myles Rudge

55 Maggon, the bad-tempered dragon

1   Once there was a dragon,
     A bad-tempered dragon,
     Maggon the Dragon
     Was his name.
     Lived inside a cavern
     On top of a mountain;
     People could see
     His smoke and flames.

       Maggon the Dragon,
       The bad-tempered dragon,
       Liked eating cows
       And bulls and sheep,
       And all through the daytime,
       He had such a gay time,
       But when night-time came
       Couldn't sleep.

2   Spiky back and long tail,
     A body of green scales,
     Maggon had such
     An appetite.
     And when he felt hungry
     He roared down the valley,
     Swallowed the cattle
     With one bite.

Words and music: Peter Canwell

DESCANT RECORDER OR GLOCKENSPIEL

1. Once there was a dra - gon, A bad - tem-pered dra - gon,

Maggon the Dragon was his name. Lived inside a cav-ern On

top of a mountain; Peo-ple could see his smoke and flames.

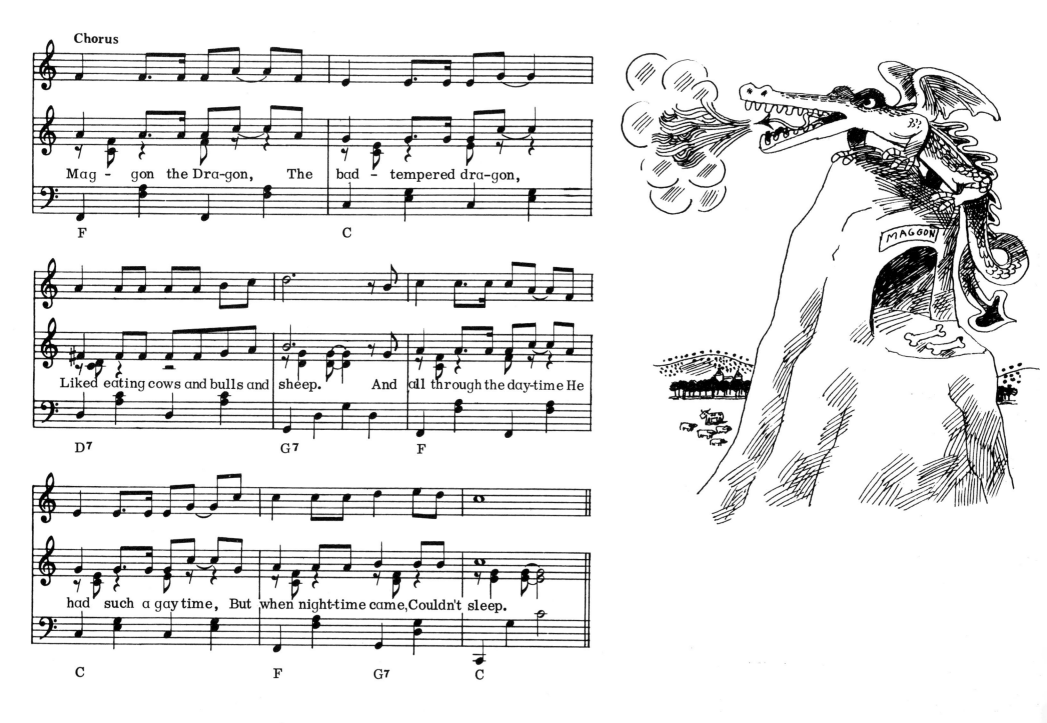

56 Risha, rasha, rusha

1. Risha, rasha, rusha,
   The hare is in the bush!
   With his beady eye he's watching,
   He's afraid you'll try to catch him.
   Risha, rasha, rusha,
   The hare is in the bush!

2. Risha, rasha, rusha,
   The hare is in the house!
   Quickly run and catch his tail
   Before he's off o'er hill and dale.
   Risha, rasha, rusha,
   The hare is in the house!

3. Risha, rasha, rusha,
   Oh, have you caught him yet?
   What! he's run into the meadow?
   Oh, you are a silly fellow!
   Risha, rasha, rusha,
   Oh, have you caught him yet?

An unconventional percussion accompaniment might be provided by two rhythm sticks, each with a sheet of sandpaper rolled round it, secured with a rubber band. The rhythm sticks should be rubbed together, keeping a steady rhythm of four quavers to each bar.

Words: Mabel Wilson
Music: G. Falke and Mabel Wilson

Acknowledgements

Grateful acknowledgement is made to the several head teachers who have helped in compiling this selection of songs, and in particular to Peggy Blakeley, Pat Lloyd – Deputy Head of Great Staughton County Primary School and Mary Collins – Head of Grange County Infant School, Gosport, Hampshire. Graham C. Westcott and Ivor Golby supplied guitar chords and Sarah Evans wrote instrumental parts and made suggestions for the use of percussion.

The following copyright owners have kindly given their permission for the reprinting of words and music:

Batt-Songs Ltd. for 27 – "The Wombling song" by Mike Batt.

BBC for 29 – "Battle Song of the Zartians" from *Time and Tune*, Spring 1965, and 48 – "Ferdinand the Donkey" from *Time and Tune*, Autumn 1964.

Bowmar Publishing Corporation, Los Angeles, California for 44 – "Five little frogs" (Ten little frogs) from *Singing Fun* by Louise Binder Scott and Lucille Wood. © Bowmar 1954.

Chappell & Co. Ltd. for 40 – "The hippopotamus song" by Michael Flanders and Donald Swann.

Wm. Collins Sons & Co. Ltd. and Random House Inc. for 6 – "The super-supper march" from *The Cat in the Hat Songbook* by Dr Seuss and Eugene Poddany. © 1967 Dr Seuss and Eugene Poddany.

Compass Music Ltd. for 25 – "Morningtown ride" by Malvina Reynolds.

Cookaway Music Ltd. and Shada Music Inc. for 2 – "I'd like to teach the world to sing (in perfect harmony)" by R. Cook, R. Greenaway, B. Backer and B. Davis. © 1971 Shada Music Inc.

Francis Day & Hunter for 8 – "Daisy Bell", 15 – "I'm Henery the Eighth, I am", 34 – "When Father papered the parlour" and 43 – "Daddy wouldn't buy me a bow-wow".

Essex Music International Ltd. for 30 – "The wind blow east" by John A. and Alan Lomax published by TRO Essex Music Ltd., 39 – "Going to the zoo" by Tom Paxton published by Harmony Music Ltd. and 54 – "A windmill in old Amsterdam" by Ted Dicks and Myles Rudge.

Faber and Faber Ltd. for 20 – "Bananas" from *Bananas in Pyjamas* by Carey Blyton.

Faber Music Ltd. on behalf of J. Curwen & Sons Ltd. for 38 – "The animals went in two by two" from *Cantemus part II*.

Noel Gay Music Co. Ltd. for 19 – "Lily the pink" by Gorman, McGear and McGough.

Mrs J. R. Green for the words of 50 – "Katie's Garden".

Edwin H. Morris & Co. Ltd. and Mark VII Ltd. California for 5 – "Sing a rainbow" by Arthur Hamilton.

Northern Songs Ltd. for 4 – "Yellow submarine" by John Lennon and Paul McCartney. © 1966 Northern Songs Ltd.

Novello & Co. Ltd. for 9 – "The bonny blue-eyed sailor", words by Rose Fyleman and melody adapted by Thomas Dunhill.

Oxford University Press for 13 – "Sparrow twitters" from *Children's Songs of Czechoslovakia* by Vera Gray and C. K. Offer, and 56 – "Risha, rasha, rusha" from *Music Time* by Mabel Wilson.

Peterman & Co. Ltd. for 28 – "Shoot! shoot! shoot!", 33 – "The fireman", 35 – "The clown", 41 – "Tiger, tiger", 49 – "The kangaroo song", 52 – "The elephant" and 55 – "Maggon, the bad-tempered dragon" by Peter Canwell and Ken Blakeson.

Keith Prowse Music Pub. Co. Ltd. for 24 – "Wheels keep turning" by Graham Beebee, and 31 – "One potato, two potato" by Paul Reade (music) and Peter Charlton (words). © 1973 Keith Prowse Music Pub. Co. Ltd.

Southern Music Publishing Company Limited for 21 – "I know an old lady" by Rose Bonne and Alan Mills.

Sterling Publishing Company Inc. for the music of 10 – "Old woman, old woman" from *Best Singing Games for Children of All Ages* by Edgar Bley. © 1957 by Sterling Publishing Co., Inc. New York.

Janet E. Tobitt for 36 – "Song of the Delhi Tongawallah".

Frederick Warne & Co. Ltd. and Gage Educational Publishing Ltd. Ontario for 32 – "The guard song" from *The High Road of Song* by Margaret Fletcher and Margaret Denison.

Graham C. Westcott for the music of 50 – "Katie's garden" and the music and words of 53 – "Gobbolino, the witch's cat".

Williamson Music Ltd. for 3 – "I whistle a happy tune" from *The King and I* by Rodgers and Hammerstein.

Song 7 – "My ship sailed from China" is expanded from "The chinese fan" included in *An Australian Campfire Book* published by the Girl Guides Association of Victoria.

The cover design is by C. R. Evans.

NB. The guitar chords, while being kept as simple as possible, have been made to fit in with the piano accompaniment wherever possible.

Index of first lines